It's time to create your own magical world! Carefully press out the pieces to build a mystical unicorn kingdom.

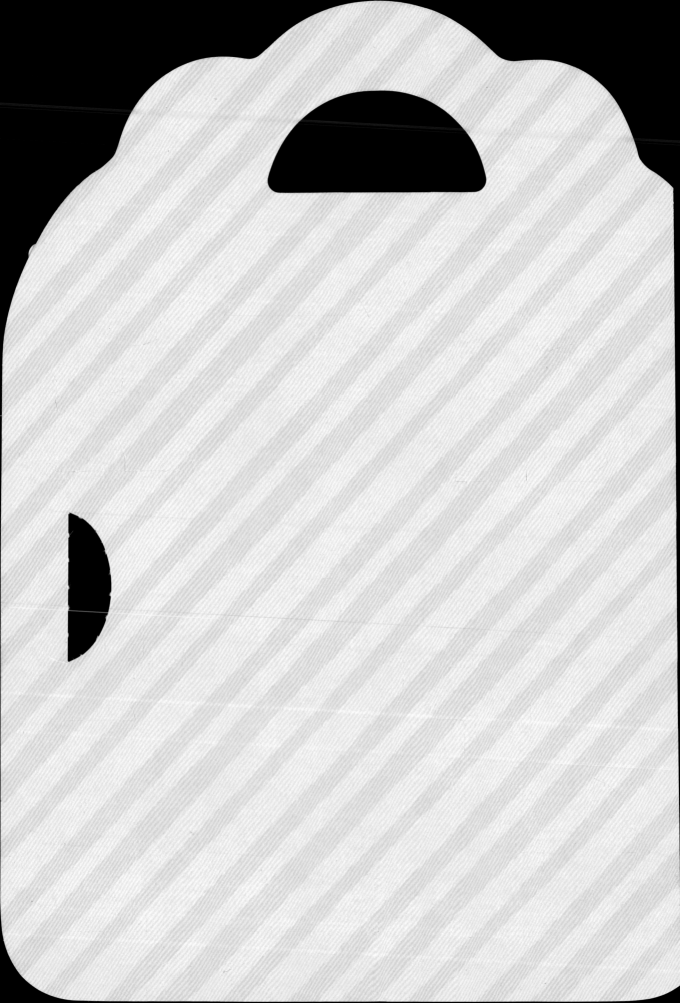

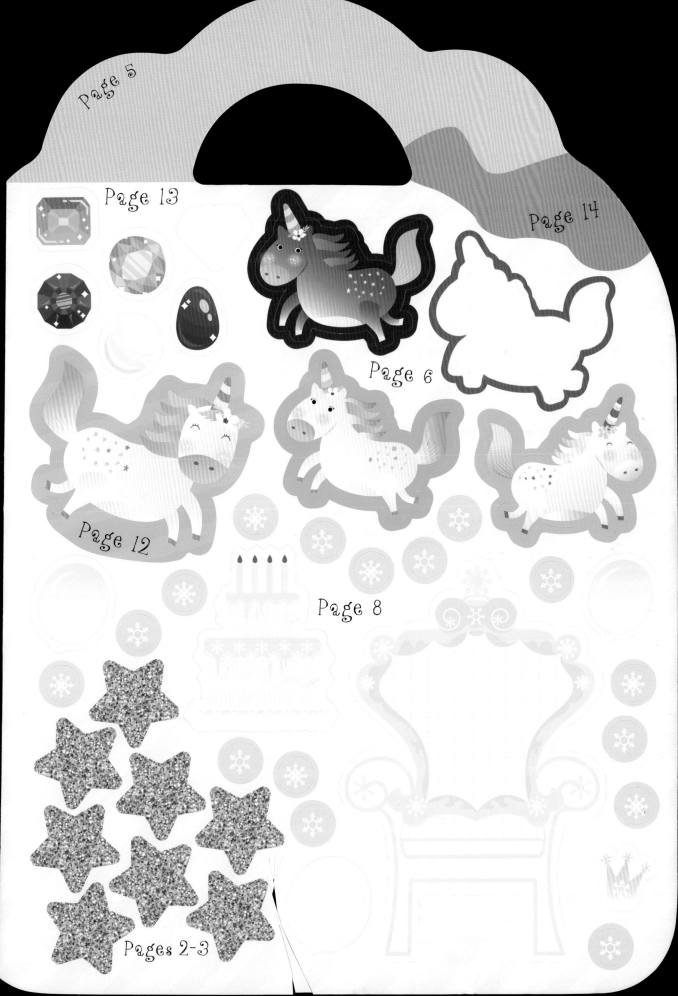

Page 5

Page 13

Page 14

Page 6

Page 12

Page 8

Pages 2-3

Sweet Feast

Munching on cupcakes all day has tired Peppermint out! Doodle a dreamy feast for this sweet-toothed unicorn.

Enchanted Forest

The glade is home to all sorts of magical creatures.
Can you spot the objects below in the big picture?

How many fairy friends can you spot playing hide and seek?

Add a star sticker each time you spot something.

3

Clever Clues

Only one of these unicorns matches Lucky's description. Use the clues below to find him.

Clues:

Lucky has a long, lilac mane.

He has a clover on his body.

He has bright blue eyes.

A

B

C

D

Up high in the sky, flying unicorns soar between the clouds. Can you spot six differences between these two pictures?

Add a heart sticker as you find each one.

Home, Sweet Home

Look at each unicorn name and picture, then find the matching unicorn sticker and place it in its perfect home.

Sunshine

Rainbow

Moondance

Snowbell

Magical Maze

This little unicorn wandered off the path and got lost! Guide him safely through the forest and back to his family.

Start →

Finish ↗

Ice Palace

The Queen of the Frost Unicorns is hosting a spectacular Snow Ball! Use your stickers to give her a crown, then fill the palace with more dazzling decorations.

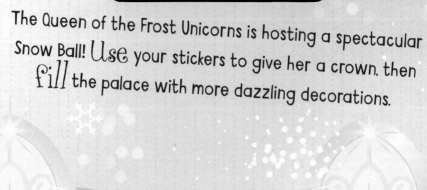

Unique Unicorns

Every unicorn is special and unique.
Design your own fabulous unicorn below.
What magical powers will they have?

Name: Buttercup
Lives: The Glistening Glade
Magical powers: Can make
flowers grow anywhere

Name: Misty
Lives: Rainbow Palace
Magical powers:
Super-fast flyer

Name: _____
Lives: _____
Magical powers: _____
_____
_____

Rainbow Race

Grab your press-out unicorn pieces and play this game with a friend.

Start →

1

9
Stuck in a rain cloud!
Go back 1 space.

2

8

How to play:

Take turns to roll the dice. Move your pieces through the clouds the same number of spaces as the number thrown. If you land on an instruction space, do what it says. The first unicorn to reach the rainbow palace wins the race.

3 Leap forward 1 space.

7 Stop to help a lost fairy. Miss a turn.

4

6

5

Odd Unicorn Out

One of these unicorns is different from the others.

Can you spot him?

Add a sticker to make him **match** the others.

A

B

C

D

E

12

Sparkly Sisters

These unicorn sisters are all named after precious gemstones.
Can you find their names in the grid below?

RUBY

EMERALD

S	A	D	I	A	M	O	N	D
E	Y	E	T	O	P	A	Z	E
M	L	P	E	A	R	L	R	D
E	B	P	L	R	N	I	Y	D
R	E	Z	R	B	H	O	Y	R
A	L	N	E	P	T	R	D	U
L	E	D	P	R	B	P	H	B
D	A	A	N	R	B	Y	E	Y
Y	S	O	T	N	U	N	I	S

Add a jewel sticker for each one you spot.

SAPPHIRE

DIAMOND

PEARL

TOPAZ

Magic Friends

Use your brightest pens or stickers to customize these unicorns.

BUBBLES

DAISY

Which unicorn do you like the most? Put a heart sticker by them.

STARDUST

CUPCAKE

14

Gorgeous Garden

The flower unicorns love playing in the secret palace garden. Doodle more pretty flowers and unicorn friends.

Answers

Pages 2-3
There are 5 fairy friends.

Page 4
Lucky is unicorn D.

Page 5

Page 6

Page 7

Page 12
Unicorn D is the odd one out.

Page 13

S	A	D	I	A	M	O	N	D
E	Y	E	T	O	P	A	Z	E
M	L	P	E	A	R	L	R	D
E	B	P	L	R	N	I	Y	D
R	E	Z	R	B	H	O	Y	R
A	L	N	E	P	T	R	D	U
L	E	D	P	R	B	P	H	B
D	A	A	N	R	B	Y	E	Y
Y	S	O	T	N	U	N	I	S

16

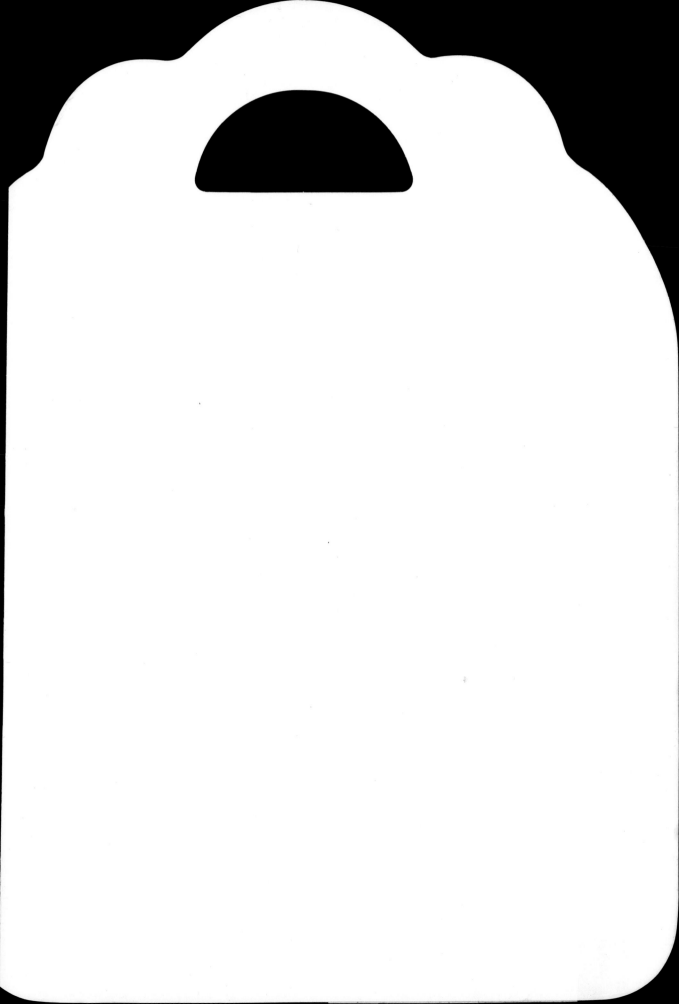